2003

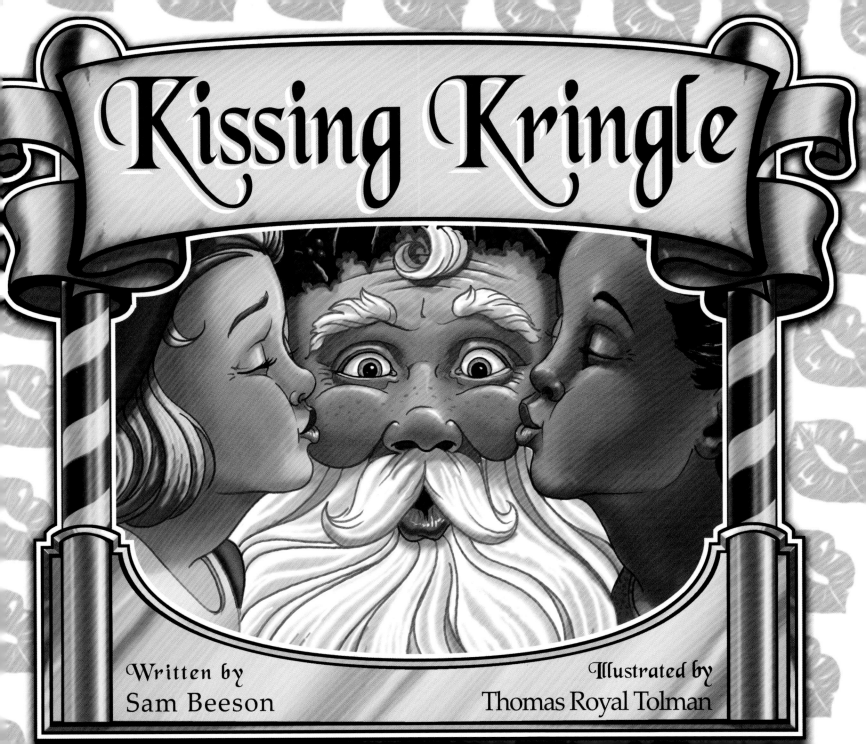

Kissing Kringle

Written by
Sam Beeson

Illustrated by
Thomas Royal Tolman

Beeson, Sam

Kissing Kringle/by Sam Beeson.-1st ed.
Summary: Santa receives strength through the power of the kiss.

Published in the United States 2003 by Gunn Books.

Illustrated & Designed by Thomas Royal Tolman & Kim Tolman

Printed by Media Source, Inc.
First Edition

This book is dedicated to Sarah.

When the lights have burned out, and Christmas is done,

When snow clouds are cleared by the melting, soft sun,

When all of the holiday worries and cares

Are tucked with the tree back under the stairs

It's then that the question so rarely arises:

"Just how does Santa prepare his surprises?"

When March marches in and the end of December

Is a season and date that we *kind-of* remember,

Did you **wonder** how Santa prepared his delivery

Before the warm air became sleety and shivery?

What secret? What **magic**? What mystical sight

Gives Santa the "umph" to tackle **Christmas** night?

The answer to this question is quite simple this:

It's the power of. . .

. . . the Kiss.

While growing up Santa was not unlike you!

He had bed making, scrubbing and sweeping to do.

He hated all work, he hated each chore,

He hated it all to the bone marrow core.

"You'll clean up this room," his **mother** would say,

"You'll clean it all up, or you won't play today!"

"But mom!" he'd cry back, "But mom!" he'd retort,

"I can't!" he would blubber and sniffle and snort.

"You can!" she would say,

"And you *will* 'cause of this. . ."

Then Santa's good mother

would give him. . .

. . . a Kiss.

A gentle sweet peck on the crown on his head

Was all that he needed to fix up his bed

And vacuum the floor, pick up every **toy**

(It didn't take much to inspire this good boy).

A **kiss** from his mother would give him the strength

To finish each chore, any task, any length.

His young life was **changed,** and all 'cause of this:

The power of. . .

. . . the Kiss.

His view of the world changed ever so slightly

And Santa made sure not to take kissing lightly.

When he **dreamt** of kissing,

he thought of sweet smooches

Not salivating slobberings like from big-lipped pooches.

Yes, when he dreamt of kissing, he thought of a **peck** -

The kind of kiss that comes from folks who say

"Oh, my HECK!"

If daily dear Santa was hugged and then kissed

None of his plans or appointments were missed,

Agendas and quotas were **cheerfully** met

Not one **girl** or **boy** could Santa forget

The reason to this reasoning is quite simply this:

It's the power of. . .

. . . the Kiss.

The Eskimos heard of this young Santa boy,

How his life with a **smooch** changed from misery to joy.

The Eskimos didn't believe that a kiss

Could change someone's sadness to bombasting **bliss**.

It didn't make sense that a face-to-face kissing

Could change what was wrong or fix what was missing.

So they shook their heads no,

they shook them with might,

They shook their **heads** morning and mid-day and night.

Then once, with heads shaking and cheeks like a rose,

One Eskimo bumped another Eskimo's **nose**!

They rubbed and they rubbed, till late in the night

They rubbed their cold noses because it felt right.

And soon life went smoothly, no fights and no bothers,

Sons rubbed with mothers, and daughters with fathers.

They all rubbed their noses, misters and miss's.

And life got much better, 'cause of. . .

. . . Eskimo Kisses.

The holiday jingle that we all remember,

That's sung every day throughout all December:

"I saw Mommy kissing Santa Claus. . ."

It only deserves a very brief pause

To see that mommy deserves a pat on the back

Her kiss to cute Claus put him back on track.

You see Santa had squeezed down too many floo's

His squeezing had given him **Christmas Eve** blues.

When mommy saw Santa with his Christmas Eve sadness

She kissed him and watched as his sad, turned to **gladness**!

Her **kiss** quickly pulled him right out of his rut

And gave him the **strength** to suck in his gut

And finish the night. All 'cause of this:

The power of. . .

. . . the Kiss.

Yes Santa grew up, and he travels the globe

With his reindeer and sleigh and his gifts and red robe,

And people now know that to make Santa happy

It doesn't take cookies or brownies or taffy.

All that he wants is one little kiss

From Granny or Mommy or brother or sis.

He also gets grinny if, instead of the shoving,

Families are kissy and huggy and loving!

So come one and all, from Iceland to Amazon!

Prepare for his coming, with your pajamas on!

This Christmas, don't leave him treats or warm drinks

'Cause now you know just how our dear Santa thinks.

The next time you're singing a Christmas time jingle

Remember, someone is out there kissing Kringle!

Take time amid all of your holiday bliss

To focus on Kris Kringle's holiday kiss!

So, now that you know that kissing's the reason

That Santa is **successful** each holiday season

Don't wait for excuses beneath **mistletoe**,

You don't need a plant to give you *get-up-and-go*.

Just think of dear Kringle, whose first name is Kris,

Then turn to a loved one and give them. . .

. . . a Kiss.